The London Nobody Knows

Gothic melancholy in St. John's Wood